TRAVEL TiME For KiDS

Girls' Big Book of Holiday Fun

Fantastic fun for children
aged 6 and over

MY BEST DAYS

Use this page to help record your holiday highlights.

Date: _____

Today I visited: _____

_____

People who came with me: _____

_____

_____

Stick ticket or souvenir here.

Weather: [ ] 😊 [ ] ☔ [ ] ⛅ [ ] ❄ [ ] ⛈

Best part: _____ Score: /10

Other good bits: _____

_____

I ate: _____

I played: _____

_____

Today was:

[ ] Simply awesome [ ] Just brilliant

[ ] Good fun [ ] Quite a laugh

[ ] Not bad [ ] Disappointing

Draw picture or paste photo here.

SHOOTING STAR

Look into clear night skies and you might be lucky enough to see a shooting star!
Can you find your way through this shooting star maze?

Start ➡

➡ **Finish**

Did you
hear the joke about
the shooting star?

It was out of
this world!

3

PLAY OUTSIDE

Play this game outdoors where there is lots of space for lots of players. This game is perfect for a picnic party!

Picnic Basket

The players sit on the ground in two even rows, facing each other, with legs stretched out and feet touching the player opposite to create something that resembles a ladder of legs.

Each player thinks secretly about one item that could be found in a picnic basket – cheese sandwich, orange drink, rug or spoon, for example.

Ask an adult to be the Picnic Basket storyteller. The storyteller creates a story that involves mentioning (as many times as possible) the sorts of things found in a picnic basket.

When players hear their item mentioned, they stand up, run to one end of the ladder and tiptoe down the ladder stepping carefully between the outstretched legs. At the end of the ladder, players run back to their original place.

The winner of Picnic Basket is the player whose chosen item is not mentioned in the story.

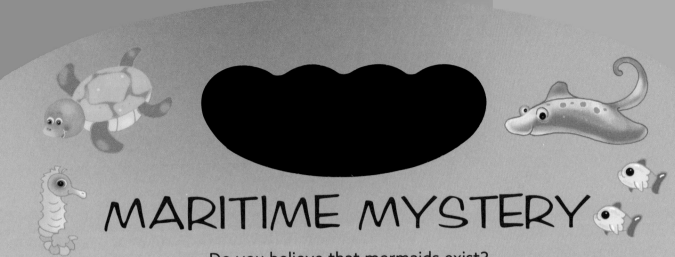

MARITIME MYSTERY

Do you believe that mermaids exist?
See if you can spot which of these is not identical to the others.

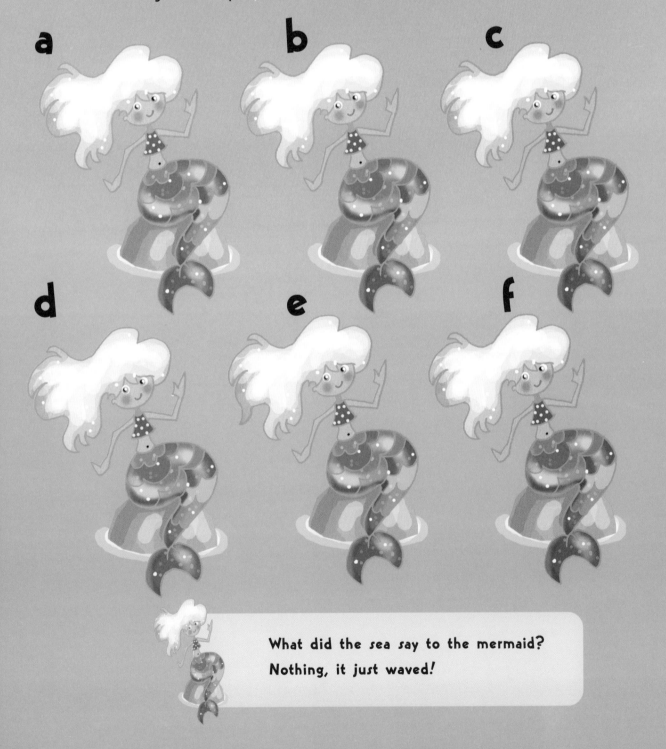

a

b

c

d

e

f

What did the sea say to the mermaid?
Nothing, it just waved!

FEELING HUNGRY?

You might be, after you've found all 10 yummy foods in the wordsearch grid.

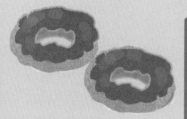

```
T A C H O T D O G P
B G B A G E L S O S
S S R Z Z P A S T A
J C O M S S T A C U
E M W E A F B R O S
L O N R U B U R D A
L P I Z Z A R Z Z G
Y M E R I N G U E E
U D S B R O E S A S
R T A P I E R M E R
```

BAGEL
BROWNIES
BURGER
MERINGUE
HOTDOG

PASTA
PIZZA
SAUSAGES
JELLY
PIE

What do you call cheese that isn't yours?
Nacho cheese!

SUPER SCOOTER

Which of the girls has scooted the farthest?
Add up the numbers on each path to find out.
The biggest total is the winner.

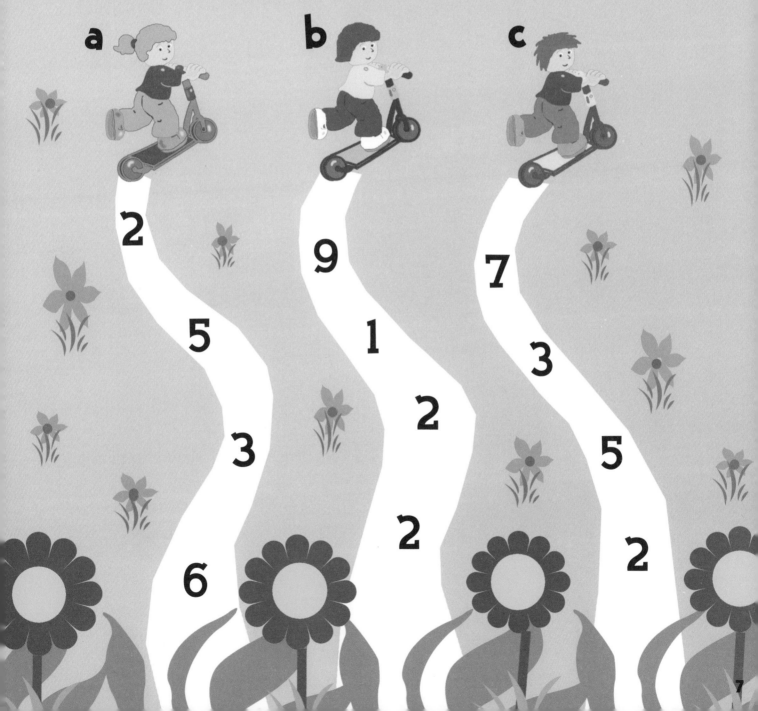

a

2
5
3
6

b

9
1
2
2

c

7
3
5
2

TRAVEL QUIZ

Do you know lots about the world you live in?
Test yourself to pass the time while you're travelling.

1. Where do polar bears live: the northern hemisphere or the southern hemisphere?

2. Which of these countries does NOT use dollars as its currency?

a. USA   b. Germany
c. New Zealand   d. Australia

3. Which country is this?

a. Russia   b. Iceland
c. Madagascar   d. Australia

4. On which continent is the Sahara Desert?

a. Africa   b. Asia
c. Europe   d. South America

5. Beijing is the capital city of which country?

a. Japan   b. India
c. China   d. Russia

6. What do you call a camel with one hump?

a. Bactrian   b. Dromedary
c. Camellary   d. Grumpy

7. Which of these countries is not in Africa?

a. Kenya   b. Cambodia
c. Botswana   d. Libya

8. Which of these mountains is an active volcano?

a. Mount Etna   b. Mount Everest
c. Mount Snowdon   d. Mount McKinley

9. How many stars are on the US flag?

a. 4   b. 20
c. 50   d. 10

10. In which city would you see this famous opera house and bridge?

a. Shirley   b. Shanty
c. Sibley   d. Sydney

11. Who built this type of pyramid?

a. Mayans   b. Inuits
c. Romans   d. Egyptians

12. Where is the Amazon, the largest river in the world?

a. North America
b. South America
c. Africa
d. Europe

Where do TVs go on holiday? To remote places!

WONDER OF THE WORLD

Which of the small silhouettes matches the large silhouette of the Taj Mahal in India?

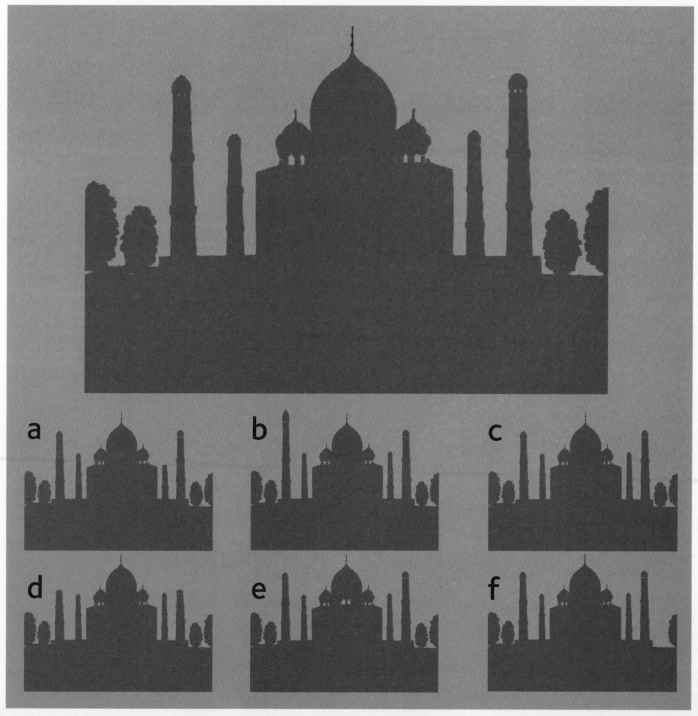

DOUBLE TROUBLE

Cross out any letters that appear twice in each grid.
The letters that are left spell the names of two European countries.

S	H	H	D	B
S	E	Q	L	Q
K	G	O	D	O
K	T	I	A	Z
U	T	Z	M	A

F	I	F	C	J
E	S	W	S	J
M	L	W	B	B
M	G	A	Y	N
G	Q	D	Q	Y

What is a twin's favourite fruit?
A pear!

GOING DOTTY

Can you find the small grid of symbols hidden in the larger grid?

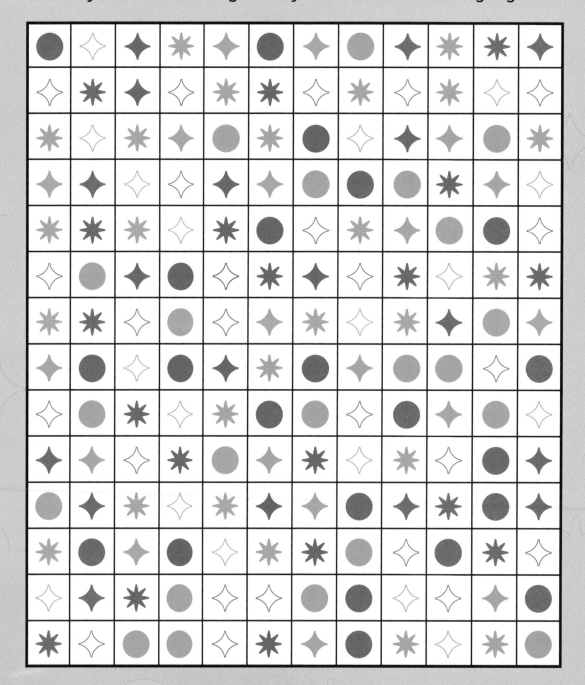

CREATURES OF THE DEEP

Only two of these octopuses are the same – can you spot them?

What do you call two octopuses that look the same? I-tentacle twins!

HAUNTED HOUSE

Can you help Millie find her way through the Haunted House at the theme park?

MAKE A POSTCARD

It's great to send a postcard to a friend back home, but it's even better to make your own! Draw a picture or cartoon inspired by your holiday onto the postcard (below). Cut it out and write your message on the back.

WE'RE HAVING FUN!

How do you cut the ocean in half?
With a sea saw!

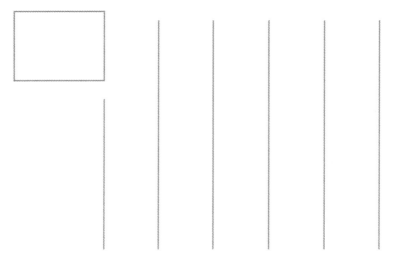

DEAR

LOVE FROM

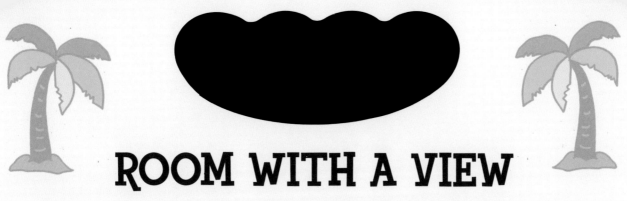

ROOM WITH A VIEW

Study the top picture to see what Isabelle can see from her hotel room.
Which of the small pictures is identical?

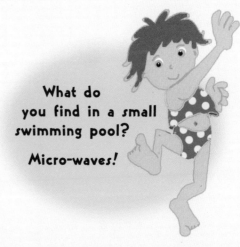

What do you find in a small swimming pool?

Micro-waves!

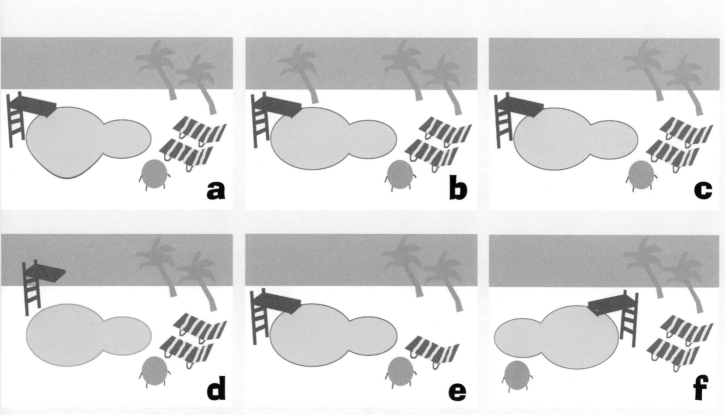

a

b

c

d

e

f

BENEATH THE WAVES

Find the 10 words hidden in the wordsearch grid.

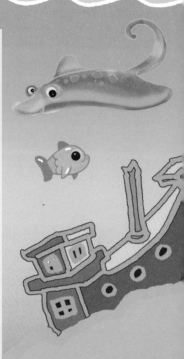

```
J Q S E A B F L J O
E D D O L P H I N Y
L U C Y E E S E N S
L R S E A W E E D T
Y C J T U N A O Y E
F H E E M F H T U R
I I L E G C O R A L
S N L L C O R S E A
H S E U P A S A K H
S H I P W R E C K B
```

CORAL   SEAWEED
DOLPHIN   SHIPWRECK
EEL   TUNA
JELLYFISH   URCHIN
OYSTER
SEAHORSE

Why did the
dolphin blush?

Because the
sea weed!

SHADY LADY

Which sunglasses will Beccy buy? Use the clues to work it out.

a

b

c

d

e

f

Beccy doesn't want pink shades.
She likes shades with stars on.
She doesn't like stripey shades.
She doesn't want blue shades.

MEGA QUIZ

Put your brain to the test with these questions about travel and the world around you.

1. In which country is the Leaning Tower of Pisa?

a. Russia
b. France
c. Italy
d. Greece

2. Niagara Falls is on the border of which countries?

a. Brazil and Peru
b. Canada and USA
c. Spain and Portugal
d. South Africa and Zimbabwe

3. Which character lives in Neverland?

a. Aslan the Lion
b. Peter Pan
c. Shrek
d. Spongebob Squarepants

4. Which of these is NOT a sport at the summer Olympics?

a. frisbee   b. water polo
c. BMX   d. judo

5. Uluru, a huge sandstone rock, is also referred to as what?

a. Ayers Rock   b. Alice Rock
c. Kid Rock   d. Camp Rock

6. Who lives at the White House?

a. US President
b. The Pope
c. Australian Prime Minister
d. Queen of England

7. Which ancient people are well known for making mummies from the dead?

a. Romans   b. Celts
c. Neanderthals   d. Egyptians

8. The Indy 500 motor race is held in which country?

a. Wales   b. Switzerland
c. Algeria   d. USA

9. In which ocean is Easter Island, home to the famous giant stone heads?

a. Pacific   b. Atlantic
c. Indian   d. Arctic

10. What would you do with a marimba?

a. eat it   b. wear it
c. play it   d. throw it

11. Which of these is not a type of shark?

a. brush
b. lemon
c. cookie cutter
d. goblin

12. Which country is sometimes called 'the land of the rising sun'?

a. Japan   b. Iceland
c. New Zealand   d. Jamaica

MY BEST DAYS

Use this page to help record your holiday highlights.

Date: _____

Today I visited: _____

_____

People who came with me:

_____

_____

Stick your
ticket here.

Weather: ☐ 🙂 ☐ ☁️ ☐ 🌧️ ☐ ❄️ ☐ 🌩️

Best part: _____ Score: ___/10

Other good bits: _____

_____

I ate: _____

I played: _____

_____

Today was:

☐ Simply awesome   ☐ Just brilliant

☐ Good fun   ☐ Quite a laugh

☐ Not bad   ☐ Disappointing

Draw a picture or paste a photo here.

MUMMY MUDDLE

Can you guide the mummy through the maze to reach the pyramids?

START

FINISH

SWEET NOTHINGS

Make this fortune teller and have some holiday fun.

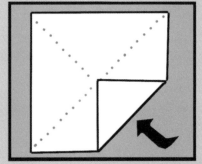

1. Cut a square of paper about the same size as the square on the opposite page. Draw lines diagonally from corner to corner, as shown above. Fold one corner so the point touches where the lines cross.

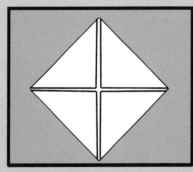

2. Fold the other three corners in the same way.

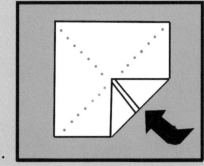

3. Turn the folded square over. Draw lines diagonally from corner to corner as you did before. Fold the corners so the points touch where the lines cross.

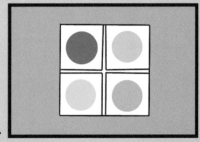

4. Turn the folded square over again. This is what it should look like. Colour a large dot on each quarter, as shown.

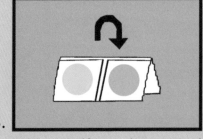

5. Fold in half, as shown, and unfold. Fold in half the other way and unfold.

6. Turn the folded square over again. Number the flaps from 1 to 8, as shown.

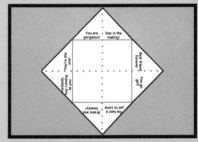

7. Open the flaps, and write mottoes like those on the page opposite. Close the flaps to see the numbers.

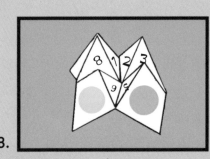

8. Turn over the square to see the coloured circles. Slot thumbs and 4th fingers into the corner pockets, and hold with the coloured circles facing up.

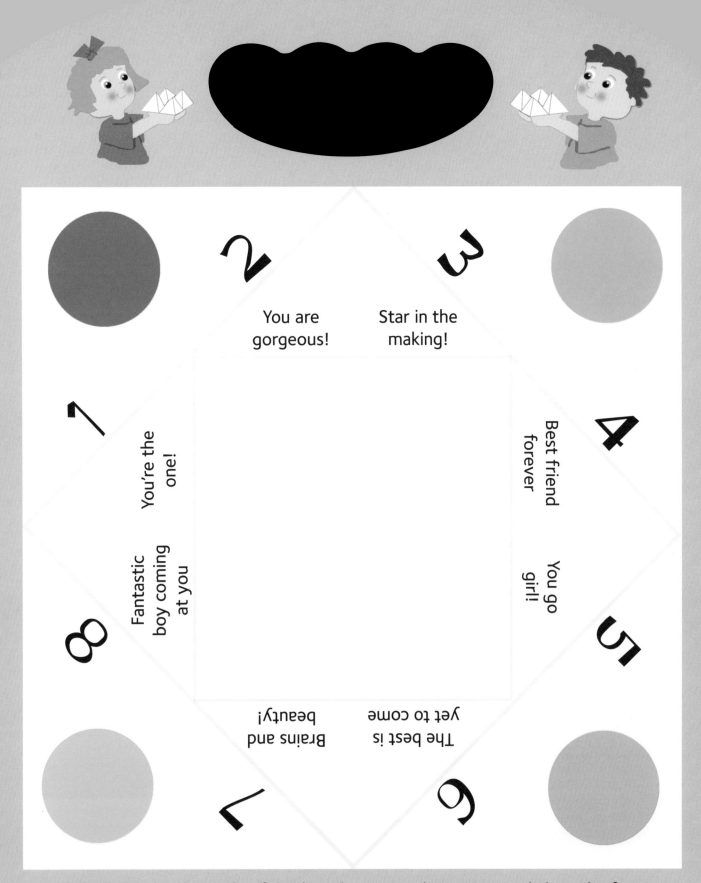

2 — You are gorgeous!

3 — Star in the making!

1 — You're the one!

4 — Best friend forever

8 — Fantastic boy coming at you

5 — You go girl!

7 — Brains and beauty!

6 — The best is yet to come

Now, you're ready to play. Ask a friend to choose a colour. Open and close the fortune teller the same number of times as there are letters in the colour word (RED = 3, for example). On the last 'letter', hold the fortune teller open and ask your friend to choose a number from the four revealed. Open and close the fortune teller that number of times. Hold the last position so your friend can choose a number. This time, open the flap for the chosen number and read the motto.

BETTY SPAGHETTI

Which bowl of spaghetti is Betty eating?

 "Waiter, waiter, will my pizza be long?"
"No, Madam, it will be round!"

WILDLIFE WORDSEARCH

If you go down to the woods today... do you think any of these will be there? Look for the 10 wild animals hidden in the grid.

```
G E R H W O L F   J Q
X H A R E W H O B   B
S W O B L T A X A   N
Q L L E I R X Y D   R
U I Y A Z A O N G   D
I Z N R E C L X E   Z
R A C C O O N Z R   H
R R A C O W Q B A   D
E D F O L L Y N X   X
L C O N W A G M Q   K
```

BADGER	LYNX
BEAR	OWL
FOX	RACCOON
HARE	SQUIRREL
LIZARD	WOLF

What animal do you look like in the bath?

A little bear!

ANYONE FOR TENNIS?

Can you find the word TENNIS hidden just once in the grid?

Why didn't the grasshopper
go to the tennis match?
He was watching the cricket!

TRAVEL BINGO

This is a terrific game when travelling and you will need two players and two pencils. The aim is to spot each of the 12 items on the game card (below). As soon as you spot one of the items, put a tick in the relevant box. The first player to tick all 12 boxes is a Bingo winner! Player 1 ticks the grey box and player 2 ticks the white box.

Why did the bee go south in the winter?
To visit an ant in Florida!

FOLLOWING FASHION

Find the correct path through the accessories, following the arrows in the right direction every time.

AMAZING FEATS

Britain's Lewis Pugh loves to swim, whatever the conditions. In 2007 he swam for 18 minutes 50 seconds in freezing Arctic waters. He swims in bizarre places to raise awareness of environmental issues such as climate change.

Travelling the world is Kashi Samaddar's passion. Kashi, from Calcutta, India, became the first person in the world to visit all 194 sovereign States. The first place visited was Uruguay; the last was Kosovo in May 2008.

Cycling backwards is a new sport! Cyclists sit on the handlebars and place their feet on the pedals. Each year, competitors take part in a 72km (45mi) backwards race in Derby, England, and in 2007 Christian Adam, from Germany, rode backwards for 61km (38mi) while playing the violin!

India's Tirtha Kumar Phani entered the record books by running over 61km (38mi) every day for a whole year. By the end of the year, he had run over 22,000 km (14,000mi)!

TAKING A TUMBLE

Can you circle 10 differences in the bottom picture?

THAT'S TORN IT!

Can you match the halves of each torn ticket, so that they spell the names of places?

Barce

ida

Corn

Singa

Port

pore

Flor

wall

What is the coldest city in Germany?

ugal

Iona

Brrrr-lin!

SCRIBBLE-TASTIC

Colour this scribble to create a piece of modern art, or make a picture out of the shapes you can see inside it.

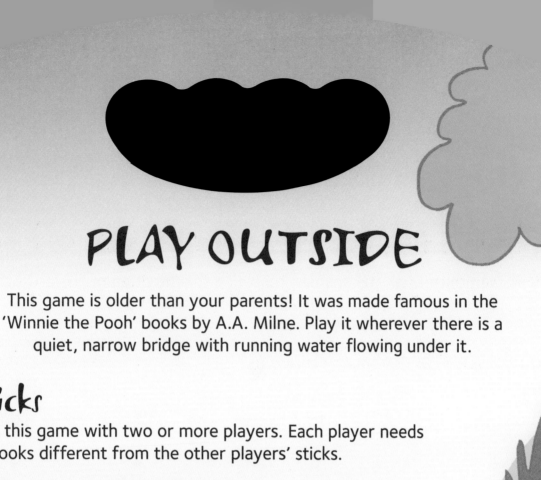

PLAY OUTSIDE

This game is older than your parents! It was made famous in the 'Winnie the Pooh' books by A.A. Milne. Play it wherever there is a quiet, narrow bridge with running water flowing under it.

Pooh Sticks

You can play this game with two or more players. Each player needs a stick that looks different from the other players' sticks.

The players line up on one side of the bridge. The water should be running towards you and disappearing under the bridge. If it's not, swap to the other side of the bridge!

Say "1-2-3-go!" and all drop your sticks into the water. Now run to the other side and wait for your stick to appear from underneath the bridge.

The winner is the player whose stick comes out first.

WARNING
Always be careful when you play near water, and make sure an adult is watching you.

SOMETHING BEGINNING WITH S

Find a path through the animals, following the direction of the arrows and animals whose name starts with 'S'.

RAINFOREST RAINBOW

Copy the colours from the smaller picture to make the larger picture look amazing.

What's the difference between the rainforest and an injured jaguar?

One pours with rain, the other roars with pain.

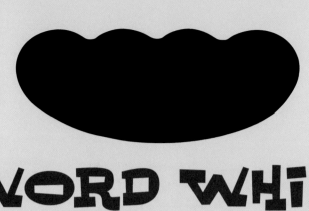

WORD WHIZ

Are you a whiz with words? See how many words you can make from the phrase 'I LOVE HOLIDAYS!'.

I LOVE HOLIDAYS!

Here are two words to get you started:

SILLY

DOVES

TREASURE SEEKERS

Challenge your friends to see who can collect the most items off this treasure hunt list. Arm the treasure hunters with a plastic container in which to store their finds.

- A leaf that isn't green!
- Three blades of grass: long, medium and short
- Something shiny
- A smooth stone
- Something made of metal
- A receipt
- A leaf that is shiny on just one side
- A Y-shaped twig
- Something pink
- A seed or nut from a tree
- A ticket
- An empty snail shell
- A feather
- A three-leaf clover

STAY SAFE!
Always tell an adult what you are doing.
Don't wander out of sight of your group.
Don't pick up sharp or dirty rubbish.
Don't harm nature to collect an item.
Wash your hands when you've finished.
Don't leave litter.

DOT TO DOT

Join the dots from 1 to 50 to see what the picture is.

X MARKS THE SPOT

Follow the clues to discover where the treasure is buried. Mark the spot with an X.

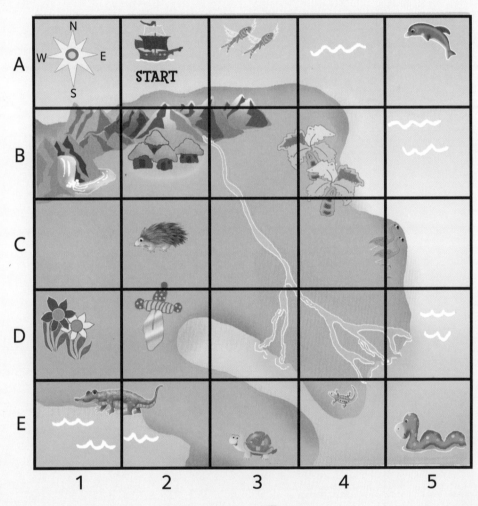

Sail east to A4 and then south to Palm Tree Bay.

Leave your ship and head south on foot to Lizard Point.

Follow the beach northwest to D2.

Head one square west and two squares north to find the treasure.

What is the grid reference?

UNDER THE SEA

What's hiding beneath the waves? Is it some beautiful fish, a scary shark,
a shivering shipwreck... or something else?

WHOLE LOTTA HOLIDAYS

There are all sorts of different holidays. Which of these is your favourite?
Try to find all 10 hidden in the grid.

```
C A R A V A N C B C Y
Y S A F A R I R E A C
C K P I N G S U A C A
H I K I N G A I C A
C I S K I O F S H M
R N A C A R A E G P
U G F D I V I N G I
S S A I L I N G C N
H I K H I S K I Y G
C Y C L I N G C Y C
```

BEACH   DIVING

CAMPING   HIKING

CARAVAN   SAFARI

CRUISE   SAILING

CYCLING   SKIING

FROZEN IN

Can you find your way through the igloo to the doorway?

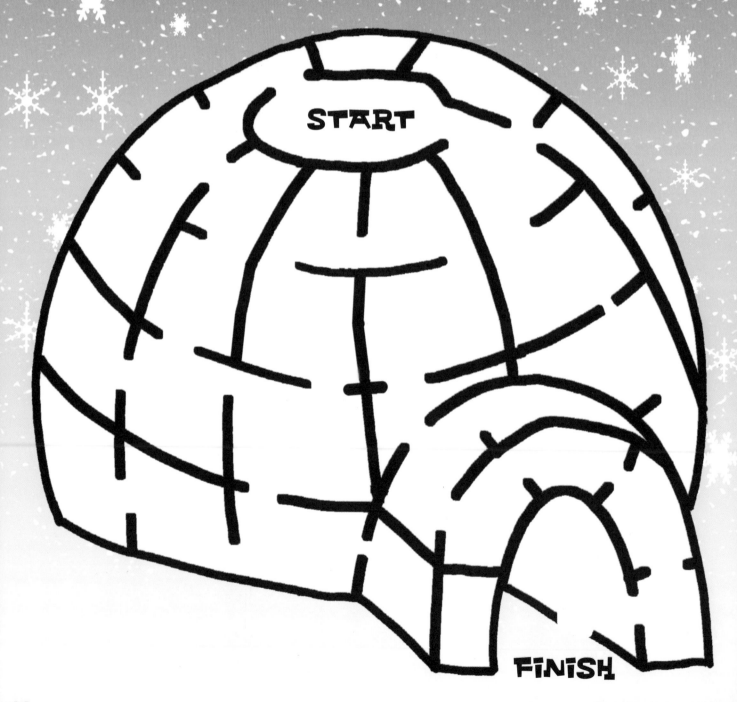

START

FINISH

THE ALPHABET GAME

Here's another game you can play on the move to keep boredom at bay.

The game is really simple. Score a point for every letter you can cross off the alphabet below, by spotting something that begins with that letter. If you see a cow, for example, you can cross off the letter 'c'.

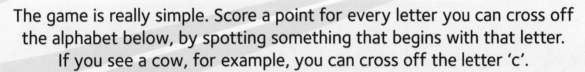

You can play on your own, and try to cross off all 26 letters, or play with travel companions and see who scores the most points. Make it harder by having to cross out the letters in order; so you can't cross off 'b' for bus until you've seen something beginning with 'a'.

Once you've played lots of times, try a different version of the game where you have to actually see each letter on a road sign, poster, shop sign or car registration plate.

FRUIT-OKU

Solve the puzzle so that every column, row and mini-grid (four squares) has one of the four fruits (pear, apple, banana and strawberry) in it.

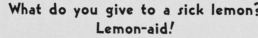

FOUR IN A ROW

Here's a simple pen and paper game to pass the time on a long journey.
You need two players, each with a different coloured pen.

Player one colours in a circle anywhere on the bottom row.

Player two takes her turn to colour a circle. It has to be next to the first circle so it can be on the bottom row, or in the row above player one's circle.

Keep taking turns to colour in a circle. Remember: you can't colour a circle that has a blank circle below it.

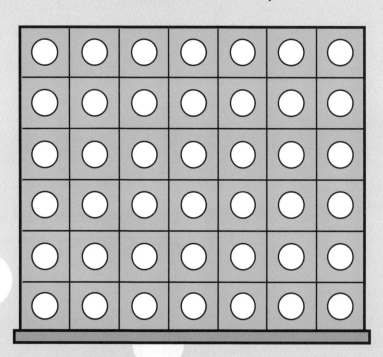

The first player to colour four in a row (across, down or diagonally) is the winner.

Play on these boards, then use scrap paper to play more games.

THE CIRCUS IS IN TOWN

The circus is full of fantastic performers.
Can you find all 10 circus words hidden in the grid?

```
U N I C Y C L E F T
A U R I N G C M I R
C N J U G G L E R A
T I G H T R O P E P
A R M A G I W F E E
B I G T O P N I A Z
O N T R A M A S T E
R I N G M A S T E R
C C B I G U N I R F
A L M A G I C I A N
```

ACROBAT	MAGICIAN
BIG TOP	RINGMASTER
CLOWN	TIGHTROPE
FIRE EATER	TRAPEZE
JUGGLER	UNICYCLE

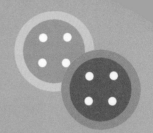

DESIGNER DOODLE

Can you finish the outfits that these girls are wearing?
Add patterns, colours, buttons and bows.

BEACH BRAINBUSTER

Are you brainy enough to work out what replaces the
question mark in the puzzle below?

?

What do you call someone who's
been at the beach all day?
Sandy!

MY BEST DAYS

Use this page to record your holiday highlights.

Date: _____

Today I visited: _____

_____

People who came with me:

_____

_____

Stick your ticket here.

Weather: [ ] 🙂 [ ] 🌧️ [ ] ☁️ [ ] ❄️ [ ] ⛈️

Best part: _____ Score: /10

Other good bits: _____

_____

I ate: _____

I played: _____

_____

Draw a picture or paste a photo here.

Today was:

[ ] Simply awesome   [ ] Just brilliant

[ ] Good fun   [ ] Quite a laugh

[ ] Not bad   [ ] Disappointing

I-SPY

Can you find 10 candy canes hidden in the picture?

MAISIE'S MAZE

Can you help Maisie through the maze to the rock pool?

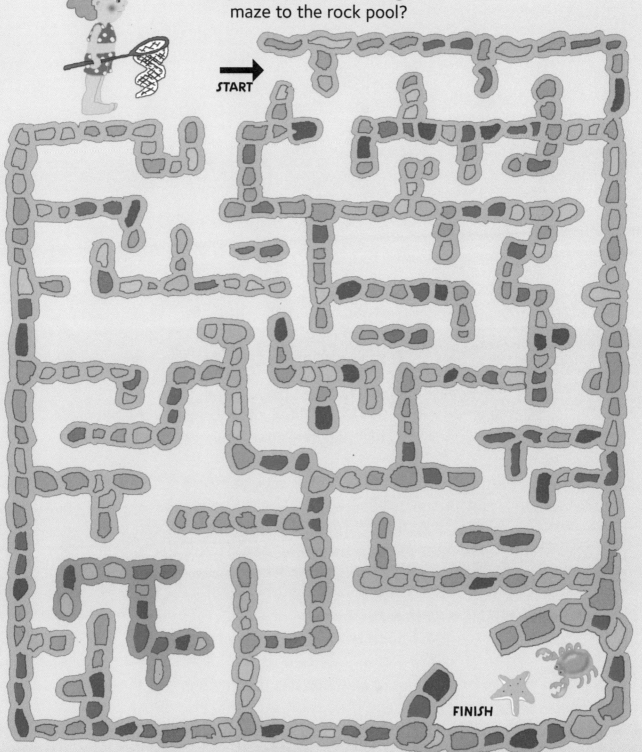

START

FINISH

PLAY OUTSIDE

Cricket is a great game for the beach or park, but it needs a lot of players. Try playing French cricket instead – you only need three players to make it work.

French Cricket

If you have more than three players that's great – it's even more fun. You'll also need a tennis ball, and a bat (a rounders or baseball bat, or a tennis racquet are fine).

One player is batting, one is bowling and everyone else is fielding. It's the job of the fielders to run after the ball and get it back to the bowler as fast as possible.

The bowler stands a few metres from the batter and throws the ball underarm, trying to hit the batter's legs. The batter has to hit the ball away to protect her legs.

The batter is not allowed to move her feet at all, but can score runs by passing the bat around her legs from hand to hand.

If the ball hits the batter's legs, or she moves her feet, or she hits the ball and someone catches it before it bounces, she is out and someone else takes a turn batting.

COOL COLOURING

Use colour to create a beautiful mosaic pattern.

MP3 MUDDLE

Debbie, Vicky and Abby have got their MP3 players in a muddle!
Can you work out which player belongs to which girl?

Debbie

Vicky

Abby

SQUARING UP

Two or three players can have great fun with this game. Each player needs a pencil. Play on this grid, then draw your own on scrap paper.

1 Player one draws a vertical or horizontal line between two adjacent dots.

2 Player two does the same, anywhere on the grid.

3 Keep joining dots until someone draws the fourth line to finish a square. The player writes his or her initials in the square and scores one point.

4 Play until the grid is full, then count the initials to see who has the most points.

ANIMAL PLANET

Do you enjoy playing guessing games? Here is a quick-fire game to play whenever you want to pass some time.

You need one player to be the 'caller'. The caller says, "land", "air" or "water".

The other players have to say an animal that lives in that element. For example, "land" answers could include rabbit, emu or lizard. "Air" answers could include wasp, seagull or bat; and frog, duck and shark would be correct examples for "water".

Score a point for each correct answer that is different from the other players' answers. If two or more players shout out the same answer, no points are awarded.
First player to get 20 points is the winner.

CATCH THE WIND

Cut out the square below, then follow the instructions on the next page to make a windmill. You will need a drinking straw, a bead and a split pin.

1. Colour both sides of the windmill, then cut along the grey lines. Fold half of each corner into the middle, like this:

2. Ask an adult to help push the split pin through the layers of paper to hold the windmill together.

3. Ask an adult to make a hole near the top of the straw.

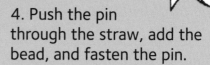

4. Push the pin through the straw, add the bead, and fasten the pin.

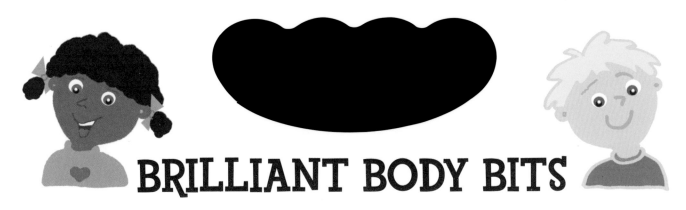

BRILLIANT BODY BITS

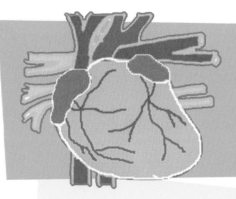

If you laid a human's blood vessels end to end, they would stretch for nearly 100,000 km (62,100 mi) and be long enough to go more than twice around the world.

Your feet have 500,000 sweat glands and they can produce half a litre of sweat each day. That's why your mum tells you to change your socks when you've been running around!

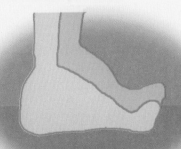

Three babies are born every second, somewhere on Earth. An average baby weighs around 3.5 kg (7.5 lb), but will be 10 times heavier by the age of 10. In the next 10 years, a person only gets twice as heavy – unless they eat too much!

Here's everything you could want to know about hair:
 * The average person's head has 100,000 to 150,000 hairs.
 * A hair grows 12-15 cm (5-6 in) a year.
 * Children lose an average of 90 hairs each day.
 * Just 1 cm (barely 1/2 in) of hair can reveal what you ate and drank, and broadly where you were over the previous month.

ANSWERS

3. Shooting Star

5. Maritime Mystery
Mermaid e

6. Feeling Hungry?

```
T A C(H O T D O G)P
B G(B A G E L)S O S
S S R Z Z(P A S T A)
J C O M S S T A C U
E M W E A F(B R O S
L O N R U B U R D A
L(P I Z Z A)R Z Z G
Y M E R I N G U E)E
U D(S)B R O E S A S
R T A(P I E R)M E R
```

7. Super Scooter
Scooter c

8/9. Travel Quiz
1. Northern   2.   b
3. d   4.   a
5. c   6.   b
7. b   8.   a
9. c   10. d
11. a   12. b

10. Wonder of the World
Silhouette c

11. Double Trouble
Belgium
Iceland

12. Going Dotty

13. Creatures of the Deep
c and d

14. Haunted House

17. Room with a View
View c

18. Beneath the Waves

```
J Q S E A B F L J O
E D(D O L P H I N)Y
L U C Y E E(S E N S
L R(S E A W E E D)T
Y C J(T U N A)O Y E
F H E E M F H T U R
I I L E G(C O R A L)
S N L L C O R S E A
H S E U P A S A K H
(S H I P W R E C K)B
```

19. Shady Lady
Pair b

20/21. Mega Quiz
1.	c	2.	b
3.	b	4.	a
5.	a	6.	a
7.	d	8.	d
9.	a	10.	c
11.	a	12.	a

23. Mummy Muddle

26. Betty Spaghetti
Bowl c

27. Wildlife Wordsearch

G E R H W O L F J Q
X H A R E W H O B B
S W O B L T A X A N
Q L L E I R X Y D R
U I Y A Z A O N G D
I Z N R E C L X E Z
R A C C O O N Z R H
R R A C O W Q B A D
E D F O L L Y N X X
L C O N W A G M Q K

28. Anyone for Tennis?

30. Following Fashion

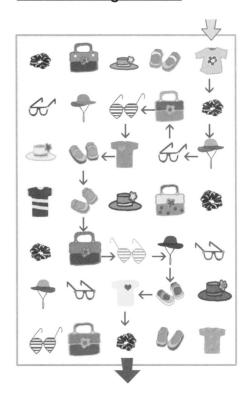

32. Taking a Tumble

33. That's Torn it!
Barcelona
Cornwall
Florida
Portugal
Singapore

36. Something Beginning with S
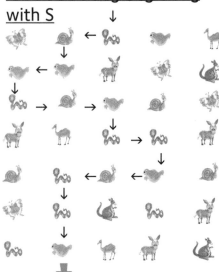

41. X Marks the Spot
Treasure is in B1

43. Whole Lotta Holidays

44. Frozen In
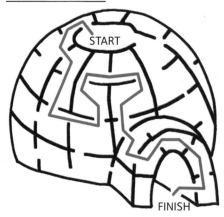

46. Fruit-oku

48. The Circus is in Town

50. Beach Brainbuster
Blue net

52. I-spy

53. Maisie's Maze

56. MP3 Muddle
Debbie – red MP3
Vicky – orange MP3
Abby – pink MP3